Jack and the Beanstalk

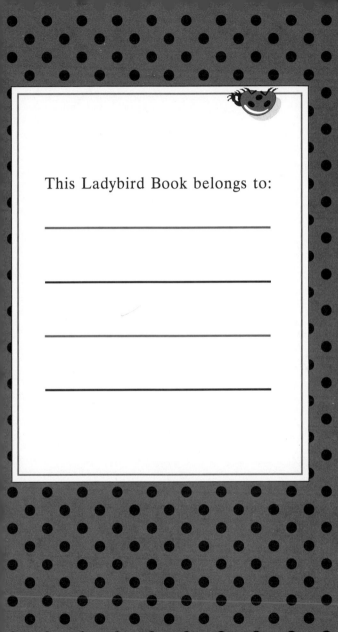

This Ladybird Book belongs to:

_____

_____

_____

_____

Ladybird Books Inc., Auburn, Maine 04210, U.S.A.
Published by Ladybird Books Ltd., Loughborough, Leicestershire, U.K.

Printed in Canada

Jack and the Beanstalk

by Fran Hunia

illustrated by Brian Price Thomas

Jack and his mother have
no money and no food
in the house.

All they have is one cow.

She is a good cow,
and she gives lots of milk,
but Jack and his mother
want food.

"Take the cow and get some money for it, and then we can buy some food to eat," says Jack's mother.

Away Jack goes with the cow. He sees a man.

"What a good cow you have," says the man.

"Yes," says Jack. "She is a good cow, and she gives lots of milk, but we can't keep her. We have to get some money for food."

"I have no money,"
says the man,
"but I have some magic beans.
Please give me the cow,
and you can have
my magic beans."

"That will be good," says Jack.
"Here you are. You take
the cow, and I'll take the
magic beans."

Jack thanks the man
and then he goes home.

Jack gives the magic beans
to his mother.
"Look," he says.
"We can eat these beans."

His mother looks
at the beans.
"Is that all you have?"
she says.
"I don't want beans."

She throws the beans away,
into the garden,
and Jack has to go to bed
with no supper.

The magic beans come up.
They grow into a big, big
beanstalk.

"What a big beanstalk," says
Jack. "It makes the house and
the trees look small. I'll go
and see what is up there."

"No," says Jack's mother. "Keep away, Jack. There will be danger up there."

"Yes," says Jack. "There will be danger, but I have to go and see what is up there."

His mother lets him go.

Jack goes up and up and up.

He sees the giant's house,
and he wants to go in.

"No, stop,"
says the giant's wife.
"You can't come in here."

"Please let me come in,"
says Jack. "I will be good."

The giant's wife likes children.
So she lets him in.

She gives him some food, and Jack thanks her.

The giant comes home. He says, "Fee, fi, fo, fum, little children, here I come."

The giant's wife puts Jack in the cupboard. She says to the giant, "There are no children here, but I have some food for you."

The giant has his supper and then he says, "Get me my money bag."

The giant's wife gets him the money bag and then she goes to bed.

Jack looks at the money bag. "The giant stole that money bag from my father," he says. "I have to get it."

The giant goes to sleep
and Jack gets
the money bag.

He runs away
down the beanstalk with it.
The giant stays asleep.

Jack gives the money bag
to his mother.
"Was this father's money
bag?" he says.

"Yes, it was,"
says his mother.
"The giant stole it."

Jack goes up
the beanstalk again.

He comes to
the giant's house,
and sees
the giant's wife.

"I don't want you
to come in,"
says the giant's wife.

"The giant will
come home and
he will go after you."

"Please let me in," says Jack.

The giant's wife likes Jack.
She lets him in
and gives him some food
and milk.

Then the giant comes home.
He says, "Fee, fi, fo, fum,
little children, here I come."

Jack gets into the cupboard.

"There are no children here,"
says the giant's wife,
"but I have some food
for you."

The giant has his supper
and then he says,
"Get me my magic hen."

The giant's wife gives it to him
and then she goes to bed.

Jack sees the magic hen.

"The giant stole that hen from my father," he says. "I have to get it."

The giant goes to sleep. Jack gets the hen and runs away with it.

The giant stays asleep.

Jack goes down
the beanstalk.
He gives the hen
to his mother.

"Can we keep this hen?"
he asks.

"Yes," says his mother.
"The giant stole that hen
from father."

Jack goes up the beanstalk
again and goes
to the giant's house.

"Please go away,"
says the giant's wife.
"You can't come in here.
The giant will get you."

But she wants to help Jack,
so she lets him come in.

The giant comes home.

He says, "Fee, fi, fo, fum,
little children, here I come."

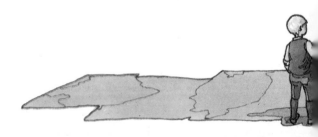

"There are no children here,"
says the giant's wife,
"but I have some food
for you."

She gives the giant his supper

The giant says, "Get me
my magic harp."

The giant's wife gives it to him
and then she goes
to bed.

The magic harp plays
for the giant,
and he goes to sleep.

Jack looks at the harp.
"That was my father's harp,"
he says. "I will get it."

Jack gets the magic harp
and runs off,
but the harp says, "Help, help!"

The giant runs after Jack.

Jack runs to the beanstalk,
and the giant runs after him.

Down goes Jack
and down goes the giant.

Jack sees his home.

He says, "Mother, mother get
the ax. The giant is after me."

Jack's mother runs to get
the ax. She gives it to him.

Down comes the beanstalk, and the giant is killed.

"That is good," says Jack's mother. "The giant is no danger to us now. Let us go and get some good things for supper."